Momentous Maths

Alison Head

In a cave far away, lives a powerful wizard named Whimstaff. He spends his days finding the answers to ancient maths problems and has parchments filled with secret symbols. In this book, Whimstaff shares his knowledge to help you master the art of maths.

Whimstaff has a goblin assistant named Pointy, who is very clever. Pointy helps Whimstaff perfect his spells and gets annoyed with the laziness of Mugly and Bugly, his fat pet frogs. They spend most of their time eating and sleeping and do as little work as possible.

Pointy also helps Whimstaff look after Miss Snufflebeam. She is a young dragon who is rather clumsy and often loses Whimstaff's numbers!

Wizard Whimstaff and his friends are very happy solving maths problems. Join them on a magical quest to win the Trophy of Maths Wizardry!

Contents

Dashing Decimals

I'm Pointy, Wizard Whimstaff's assistant! I'm here to help you find out about decimals. They break whole numbers up into smaller parts, just like fractions or percentages.

| hundredths |
| tenths |
| units |

1.24 means one whole number plus two tenths and four hundredths.

Decimals can be rounded up or down to make a whole number. Any decimal .5 or higher should be rounded up and anything .4 or below is rounded down.

So 1.4 becomes 1 and 1.5 becomes 2.

You'll soon get the hang of it!

Task 1
Ordering decimals is easy when you know how! Look at these sequences, then rewrite them in the correct order, from the smallest value to the largest.

a 2.31   1.32   1.23   1.13   2.23   2.13

_____ _____ _____ _____ _____ _____

b 18.14   14.18   14.81   18.84   14.14   18.41

_____ _____ _____ _____ _____ _____

c 3.15   1.35   5.35   5.53   1.55   3.51

_____ _____ _____ _____ _____ _____

Task 2
One of the decimals in these sequences is covered up. Can you write it back in?

a 3.45 [   ] 3.47   **b** 12.21 [   ] 12.23   **c** 8.02 [   ] 8.04

Now try these. This time the missing number has three places after the decimal point.

d 3.184 [   ] 3.186   **e** 5.245 [   ] 5.247   **f** 11.321 [   ] 11.323

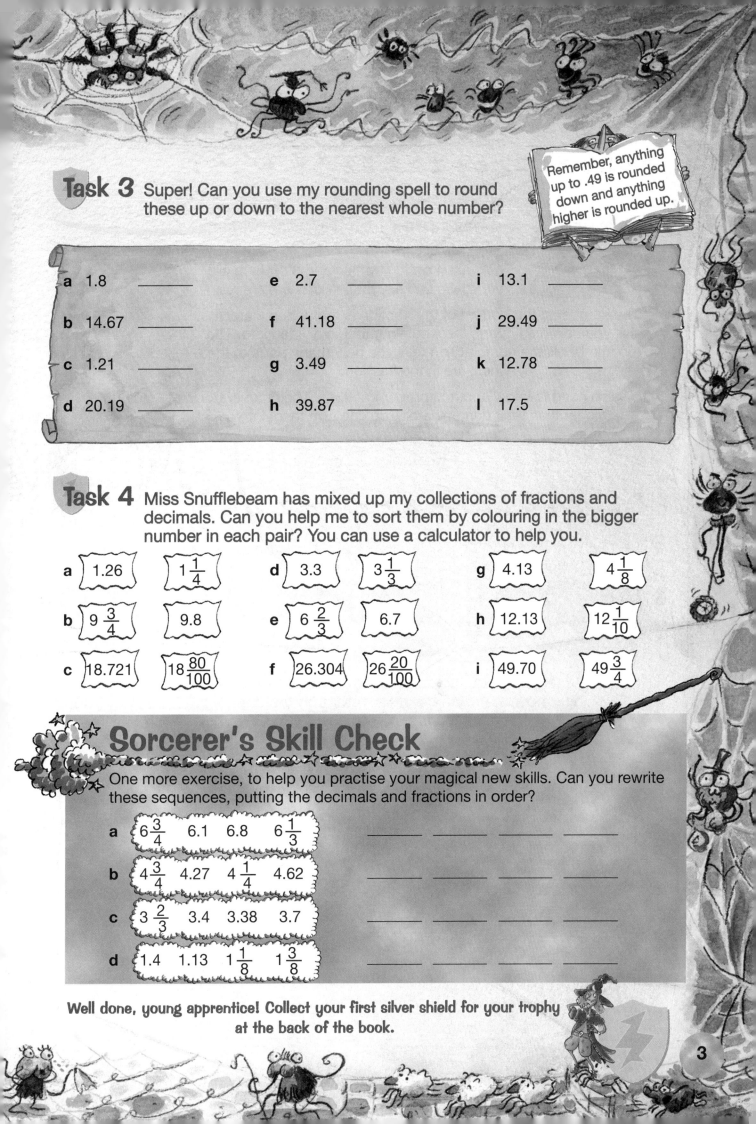

Task 3 Super! Can you use my rounding spell to round these up or down to the nearest whole number?

> Remember, anything up to .49 is rounded down and anything higher is rounded up.

a 1.8 _____

b 14.67 _____

c 1.21 _____

d 20.19 _____

e 2.7 _____

f 41.18 _____

g 3.49 _____

h 39.87 _____

i 13.1 _____

j 29.49 _____

k 12.78 _____

l 17.5 _____

Task 4 Miss Snufflebeam has mixed up my collections of fractions and decimals. Can you help me to sort them by colouring in the bigger number in each pair? You can use a calculator to help you.

a 1.26 | $1\frac{1}{4}$

b $9\frac{3}{4}$ | 9.8

c 18.721 | $18\frac{80}{100}$

d 3.3 | $3\frac{1}{3}$

e $6\frac{2}{3}$ | 6.7

f 26.304 | $26\frac{20}{100}$

g 4.13 | $4\frac{1}{8}$

h 12.13 | $12\frac{1}{10}$

i 49.70 | $49\frac{3}{4}$

Sorcerer's Skill Check

One more exercise, to help you practise your magical new skills. Can you rewrite these sequences, putting the decimals and fractions in order?

a $6\frac{3}{4}$ 6.1   6.8 $6\frac{1}{3}$ _____ _____ _____ _____

b $4\frac{3}{4}$ 4.27 $4\frac{1}{4}$ 4.62   _____ _____ _____ _____

c $3\frac{2}{3}$ 3.4   3.38   3.7   _____ _____ _____ _____

d 1.4   1.13 $1\frac{1}{8}$ $1\frac{3}{8}$ _____ _____ _____ _____

Well done, young apprentice! Collect your first silver shield for your trophy at the back of the book.

Fearsome Fractions

Slurp! We're Mugly and Bugly, Pointy's lazy frogs. We've been woken up to tell you about fractions. They are another way of breaking up numbers into smaller parts.

There are 4 potion bottles and 3 of them are red, so we can say that $\frac{3}{4}$ of them are red.

The number at the bottom of the fraction is the denominator. It tells you how many parts the whole number is divided into. The top number is the numerator. It tells you how many parts of the whole are in the fraction.

You also need to know about improper fractions. Their numerator is bigger than their denominator. You can turn them into a mixed fraction.

$$\frac{5}{4} = \frac{4}{4} + \frac{1}{4} = 1 \text{ whole plus } \frac{1}{4}, \text{ or } 1\frac{1}{4}.$$

Task 1
If you want to be as clever as Pointy, you need to turn these into mixed fractions.

a $\frac{17}{4}$ b $\frac{25}{8}$ c $\frac{9}{7}$ d $\frac{11}{2}$

e $\frac{33}{8}$ f $\frac{27}{5}$ g $\frac{33}{12}$ h $\frac{41}{10}$

Task 2
Croak! Can you reduce these fractions to their simplest form, by finding a number that both the numerator and the denominator can be divided by? We've done the first one to show you how.

a $\frac{4}{16}$ $4 \div \boxed{4} = \boxed{1}$ $16 \div \boxed{4} = \boxed{4}$ $\frac{4}{16} = \boxed{\frac{1}{4}}$

b $\frac{6}{18}$ $6 \div \boxed{} = \boxed{}$ $18 \div \boxed{} = \boxed{}$ $\frac{6}{18} = \boxed{}$

c $\frac{4}{12}$ $4 \div \boxed{} = \boxed{}$ $12 \div \boxed{} = \boxed{}$ $\frac{4}{12} = \boxed{}$

d $\frac{10}{15}$ $10 \div \boxed{} = \boxed{}$ $15 \div \boxed{} = \boxed{}$ $\frac{10}{15} = \boxed{}$

e $\frac{6}{9}$ $6 \div \boxed{} = \boxed{}$ $9 \div \boxed{} = \boxed{}$ $\frac{6}{9} = \boxed{}$

f $\frac{12}{18}$ $12 \div \boxed{} = \boxed{}$ $18 \div \boxed{} = \boxed{}$ $\frac{12}{18} = \boxed{}$

g $\frac{16}{24}$ $16 \div \boxed{} = \boxed{}$ $24 \div \boxed{} = \boxed{}$ $\frac{16}{24} = \boxed{}$

Task 3

Can you convert these so they all have a common denominator and put them in order starting with the smallest. Burp!

We're always on the look out for easy ways to do things. It's easier to put fractions in order if they all have a common denominator.

a $\frac{1}{5}$ $\frac{6}{10}$ $\frac{6}{15}$ $\frac{20}{25}$

_____

b $\frac{4}{5}$ $\frac{3}{10}$ $\frac{8}{20}$ $\frac{70}{100}$

_____

c $\frac{1}{6}$ $\frac{4}{12}$ $\frac{12}{18}$ $\frac{10}{12}$

_____

d $\frac{4}{10}$ $\frac{4}{5}$ $\frac{60}{100}$ $\frac{4}{20}$

_____

Task 4

Brain cell alert! Denominators are also useful when you're trying to find a fraction of a number or quantity. Try these.

For example, if you were trying to work out $\frac{3}{8}$ of 16:
16 ÷ 8 = 2, so $\frac{1}{8}$ of 16 = 2. 3 × 2 = 6, so $\frac{3}{8}$ of 16 is 6.

a $\frac{1}{6}$ of 24 _____

b $\frac{3}{4}$ of 12 _____

c $\frac{2}{5}$ of 20 _____

d $\frac{4}{10}$ of 200 _____

e $\frac{2}{3}$ of 18 _____

Sorcerer's Skill Check

Grub's up! While we're munching, try this last exercise. Join up the pairs of mixed and improper fractions that show the same amount.

a $\frac{13}{3}$ **b** $\frac{9}{4}$ **c** $\frac{17}{5}$ **d** $\frac{1}{10}$ **e** $\frac{1}{3}$ **f** $1\frac{1}{5}$ **g** $\frac{30}{100}$

$\frac{3}{10}$ $2\frac{1}{4}$ $\frac{6}{5}$ $4\frac{1}{3}$ $\frac{2}{20}$ $3\frac{2}{5}$ $\frac{2}{6}$

Abracadada! Pop another silver shield on your trophy!

Ratio and Proportion

I'm Wizard Whimstaff
and I'm here to make you a maths whizz!
I need to teach you about **ratio and proportion**.

Ratio is a way of comparing different numbers in a group. Look at this group of spiders.

The ratio of pink spiders to blue spiders is 2 to 3. You can also write this as 2 : 3.

Proportion looks at one number as part of the whole. 2 spiders in 5 are pink.

Task 1 Hey presto! Let's start by looking at ratios. Can you write the ratio that is represented by these groups?

a

blue : yellow = ☐ : ☐

b
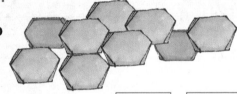

blue : green = ☐ : ☐

c

tall : short = ☐ : ☐

d

red : yellow = ☐ : ☐

Task 2 Here are the ratios I need to make one bottle of each of my favourite spells. Can you help me work out the ingredients I'll need to make bigger batches? Just multiply both sides of the ratio by the same number.

Vanishing drops
8 toads' warts : 12 yeti hairs

Tongue-tie brew
16 snakes' tongues : 4 wolf howls

Sound asleep spell
3 swamp rats : 4 eyeballs

What is the ratio of ingredients for:

a 12 bottles of vanishing drops

b 3 bottles of tongue-tie brew

c 6 bottles of sound asleep spell

Task 3 Now let's turn our attention to proportion. Miss Snufflebeam has been trying out her magnifying spell, without much success. What proportion of each group of objects has the spell worked on?

a

[ ] in [ ]

b

[ ] in [ ]

c

[ ] in [ ]

d

[ ] in [ ]

e

[ ] in [ ]

f

[ ] in [ ]

Task 4 Mugly and Bugly have been snacking again. Can you shade each pizza to represent the proportion they have eaten?

a

3 in 5 slices of pizza

b

6 in 8 slices of pizza

c

4 in 9 slices of pizza

Sorcerer's Skill Check

Allakazan! Look at these magical words and write down both the ratio and proportion of vowels and consonant in each word.

a WIZARD

The ratio of vowels to consonants is __2__ : __4__
The proportion of vowels is __2__ in __6__

b MAGICAL

The ratio of vowels to consonants is ____ : ____
The proportion of vowels is ____ in ____

c POTION

The ratio of vowels to consonants is ____ : ____
The proportion of vowels is ____ in ____

d CAULDRON

The ratio of vowels to consonants is ____ : ____
The proportion of vowels is ____ in ____

Burp! You'll soon be as brainy as Pointy! Add another silver shield to your trophy.

Playful Percentages

Pointy here again!
A **percentage** is the number of parts in 100 and it's easy to work out when you know how! Suppose you want to find 20% of 400. Start by breaking the number into 100 equal parts. Each is 1% of the total.

400 ÷ 100 = 4, so 1% of 400 is 4.

Then just multiply by whatever percentage you need to find!

20 × 4 = 80
20% of 400 = 80

Super! Now try these!

Task 1 These wands are divided into 100 equal parts. Can you work your magic and colour in the wands to represent these percentages?

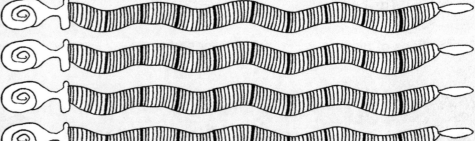

a 10%

b 20%

c 25%

d 40%

e 60%

f 75%

Task 2 Fractions can also represent parts of whole numbers. Can you draw lines to join up the matching pairs? Practice makes perfect!

a $\frac{1}{4}$ b $\frac{7}{10}$ c $\frac{4}{100}$ d $\frac{2}{3}$ e $\frac{20}{100}$ f $\frac{1}{2}$ g $\frac{30}{100}$

70%   30%   50%   20%   25%   4%   66.6%

8

Task 3 Super! Now can you write down what percentage these fractions represent?

a $\frac{1}{2}$ ⟩ d $\frac{3}{4}$ ⟩ g $\frac{1}{3}$ ⟩ j $\frac{9}{10}$ ⟩

b $\frac{3}{5}$ ⟩ e $\frac{2}{5}$ ⟩ h $\frac{30}{100}$ ⟩ k $\frac{75}{100}$ ⟩

c $\frac{2}{10}$ ⟩ f $\frac{60}{100}$ ⟩ i $\frac{4}{5}$ ⟩ l $\frac{1}{4}$ ⟩

Task 4 Now let's see if you can work out some percentages. Remember, find 1% first, then multiply to find the percentage you need.

a 10% of £50

b 40% of £500

c 45% of £400

d 20% of £70

e 80% of £500

f 10% of £720

g 50% of £120

h 75% of £600

i 15% of £200

Sorcerer's Skill Check

Just one exercise to go. Can you pick the book from each pair that has the bigger number and colour it in? You can use a separate piece of paper for your workings.

a $\frac{4}{10}$ 30%

b 20% $\frac{1}{10}$

c 78% $\frac{3}{4}$

d $\frac{8}{10}$ 90%

e 10% $\frac{1}{15}$

f $\frac{1}{3}$ 50%

g $\frac{9}{10}$ 88%

h $\frac{2}{3}$ 65%

100% effort there, young apprentice! Add another silver shield to your trophy.

Brilliant Brackets

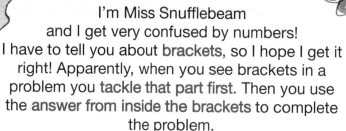

I'm Miss Snufflebeam and I get very confused by numbers! I have to tell you about **brackets**, so I hope I get it right! Apparently, when you see brackets in a problem you tackle that part first. Then you use the **answer from inside the brackets** to complete the problem.

$$12 - (4 \times 2) = ?$$
$$4 \times 2 = 8$$
$$12 - 8 = 4$$

Now can you help me work these out?

Task 1 I'm in a terrible muddle with these problems. First help me to work out the answer to the mini problem inside the brackets. Then replace the brackets with your answer. Then work out the final answer in column three.

a $12 \times (3 + 4) =$	$3 + 4 = 7$ 12×7 =	84
b $10 \times (4 - 2) =$	_____ _____ =	_____
c $8 \div (6 - 4) =$	_____ _____ =	_____
d $36 \div (10 + 2) =$	_____ _____ =	_____
e $40 \div (4 \times 2) =$	_____ _____ =	_____
f $12 + (12 \times 3) =$	_____ _____ =	_____
g $64 - (4 \times 8) =$	_____ _____ =	_____

Task 2 Abracadada! You're really clever. Now can you work out the answers to these problems?

a $3 + (12 \div 2) =$ ☐   **d** $21 \div (5 + 2) =$ ☐   **g** $12 - (4 + 1) =$ ☐

b $100 \div (12 - 2) =$ ☐   **e** $3 \times (2 + 2) =$ ☐   **h** $12 + (6 \div 2) =$ ☐

c $18 - (12 - 3) =$ ☐   **f** $15 \div (10 \div 2) =$ ☐   **i** $9 \times (8 \div 2) =$ ☐

Task 3 Now I'm really confused! These problems each have two sets of brackets. Can you help me work out the problems in the brackets first, then rewrite the problem to find the answer?

a $(3 + 2) - (6 \div 2) =$ ☐ $-$ ☐ $=$ ☐   d $(12 \times 3) \div (2 + 2) =$ ☐ $\div$ ☐ $=$ ☐

b $(2 \times 3) + (10 \div 2) =$ ☐ $+$ ☐ $=$ ☐   e $(12 \div 2) \times (2 + 3) =$ ☐ $\times$ ☐ $=$ ☐

c $(60 \div 10) \div (4 - 2) =$ ☐ $\div$ ☐ $=$ ☐   f $(3 \times 3) \times (10 \div 2) =$ ☐ $\times$ ☐ $=$ ☐

Task 4 Help! I tried to use some magic to help me work out these problems, but instead I've made the numbers in the brackets disappear! Can you write in a mini problem that will give the correct answer?

a $3 + ($ ☁ $) = 8$ e $30 - ($ ☁ $) = 21$

b $12 \div ($ ☁ $) = 4$ f $2 \times ($ ☁ $) = 12$

c $24 \div ($ ☁ $) = 3$ g $15 - ($ ☁ $) = 10$

d $4 \times ($ ☁ $) = 32$ h $50 \div ($ ☁ $) = 5$

Sorcerer's Skill Check

Oh dear! I still can't get my magic right. This time, all the brackets have got muddled up in the cauldron. Can you pick a set of brackets to complete each problem?

a $12 +$ ⬭ $= 16$

b $5 \times$ ⬭ $= 35$

c $10 -$ ⬭ $= 7$

d $12 \div$ ⬭ $= 2$

e $18 -$ ⬭ $= 8$

f $27 +$ ⬭ $= 35$

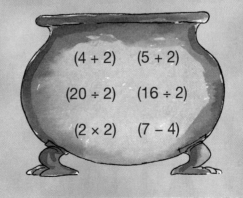

$(4 + 2)$ $(5 + 2)$

$(20 \div 2)$ $(16 \div 2)$

(2×2) $(7 - 4)$

Time for you to collect another silver shield... and for us to grab a snack!

Dastardly Decimals

Multiplying **decimals**
by 10 or 100 is easy when you know how!
Just move each digit to the left – **one place**
to multiply by **10** and **two places** to multiply by 100.
Here's how you multiply 1.24 by 10 and 100.

1.24 × 10 =

1.24 × 100 =

Task 1

Let's start by mastering multiplying decimals by 10. You'll soon get the hang of it!

	tens	units	tenths	hundredths
a		2 •	3	3
b		1 •	4	3
c		4 •	4	3
d		7 •	1	9

2.33 × 10 =

1.43 × 10 =

4.43 × 10 =

7.19 × 10 =

Task 2

Well done! Now you've mastered the above, try multiplying these by 100. It's easy when you know how!

	hundreds	tens	units	tenths	hundredths
a			2 •	3	3
b			1 •	4	3
c			4 •	4	3

2.33 × 100 =

1.43 × 100 =

4.43 × 100 =

Task 3 Super effort! Now let's see if you can do it in your head!

a 9.82 × 10 = ☐   **d** 12.04 × 10 = ☐   **g** 18.31 × 10 = ☐

b 4.10 × 10 = ☐   **e** 0.10 × 10 = ☐   **h** 3.41 × 100 = ☐

c 12.82 × 100 = ☐   **f** 91.12 × 100 = ☐   **i** 10.03 × 100 = ☐

Task 4 Something a little different now. These problems have been done for you. You just have to decide if the stars are covering up 10 or 100. Write in the number when you've made up your mind!

a 0.41 × ⭐ = 4.10   **d** 3.01 × ⭐ = 301.00   **g** 4.08 × ⭐ = 40.8

b 14.37 × ⭐ = 143.7   **e** 72.81 × ⭐ = 728.1   **h** 84.31 × ⭐ = 8431.00

c 3.189 × ⭐ = 31.89   **f** 12.743 × ⭐ = 1274.30   **i** 7.001 × ⭐ = 70.01

Sorcerer's Skill Check

My multiplying cauldron makes short work of multiplying decimals by 10 or 100. You can see the results, but can you work out what number the machine started with each time?

a ☐ → 10.1   **f** ☐ → 12.34

b ☐ → 73.41   **g** ☐ → 94.31

c ☐ → 18.94   **h** ☐ → 121.2

d ☐ → 1.3   **i** ☐ → 314.4

e ☐ → 41.74   **j** ☐ → 712

× 10   × 100

Your decimal powers are dazzling! Another silver shield!

Apprentice Wizard Challenge 1

Challenge 1 Circle the largest number from each sequence, then write your answers in the correct order starting with the smallest.

a 64.38   63.84   68.34   68.43   64.83   _____

b 71.49   71.19   71.98   71.91   71.94   _____

c 67.381   67.814   68.183   68.813   68.816   _____

d 70.143   70.413   71.314   71.918   71.911   _____

e 70.013   71.103   71.991   70.908   71.919   _____

Challenge 2 Find the magical missing fractions in the table of improper and mixed fractions.

	Improper	Mixed
a	$\frac{7}{2}$	
b		$6\frac{1}{4}$
c	$\frac{5}{3}$	
d		$12\frac{1}{4}$
e	$\frac{15}{7}$	

	Improper	Mixed
f		$8\frac{4}{5}$
g	$\frac{19}{8}$	
h		$4\frac{2}{3}$
i	$\frac{36}{5}$	
j		$12\frac{7}{8}$

Challenge 3 Here is some information about the proportions of various objects in the cave. Can you use it to answer these questions?

a 1 potion bottle in 4 is blue. If there are 12 bottles, how many will be blue?

_____

b 2 crystals out of 8 are purple. If there are 16 crystals, how many are purple?

_____

c 2 frogs in 5 are red. If there are 20 frogs, how many will be red?

_____

d 3 webs out of 7 have spiders. If there are 28 webs, how many have spiders?

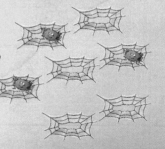

_____

Challenge 4 Can you work out these percentage problems?

a 10% of £240 _____

b 20% of £80 _____

c 45% of £200 _____

d 3% of £400 _____

e 40% of £80 _____

f 60% of 140 _____

g 15% of £600 _____

h 90% of 180 _____

i 25% of 440 _____

Challenge 5 Pointy's got brackets on the brain! Can you solve the brackets and fill in the gaps to complete these problems?

a $3 \times (4 + 2) = 3 \times \bigcirc = \bigcirc$

b $27 - (21 \div 3) = 27 - \bigcirc = \bigcirc$

c $\bigcirc \times (12 - 8) = \bigcirc \times \bigcirc = 40$

d $24 - (\bigcirc - 4) = 24 - \bigcirc = 19$

e $12 \times (2 \times \bigcirc) = 12 \times \bigcirc = 96$

f $8 \div (6 - 4) = 8 \div \bigcirc = \bigcirc$

g $\bigcirc + (18 \div 2) = \bigcirc + \bigcirc = 11$

h $\bigcirc \div (3 + 3) = \bigcirc \div \bigcirc = 6$

i $49 \div (\bigcirc \div 3) = 49 \div \bigcirc = 7$

j $7 \times (3 \times \bigcirc) = 7 \times \bigcirc = 63$

Challenge 6 Solve these decimal multiplication problems.

a $1.4 \times 10 =$ ____ $1.4 \times 100 =$ ____

b $0.41 \times 10 =$ ____ $0.41 \times 100 =$ ____

c $3.031 \times 10 =$ ____ $3.031 \times 100 =$ ____

d $0.048 \times 10 =$ ____ $0.048 \times 100 =$ ____

Count how many challenges you got right and put stars on the test tube to show your score. Then have a silver shield for your trophy!

6
5
4
3
2
1

Challenge Score

Mesmerising Multiplication

Allakazan!
The best maths wizards use written multiplication methods for large numbers. Here are two magical methods of working out 43 × 22.

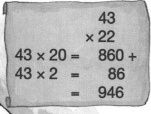

```
            43
          × 22
43 × 20 =  860 +
43 × 2  =   86
        =  946
```

43 × 22		
×	40	3
20	800 + 60	= 860
2	80 + 6	= 86 +
		= 946

Task 1

Let's start by using the first method to work out these multiplication problems. Don't worry if it seems hard at first. Just do the best you can!

a 65 × 33

```
        65
      × 33
65 × 30
65 × 3  _____
```

b 53 × 19

```
           53
         × 19
53 × 10
53 × 9   _____
```

c 45 × 52

```
           45
         × 52
45 × 50
45 × 2   _____
```

Task 2

Abracadabra! Fine work so far! Time to give the other method a try.

a 71 × 31

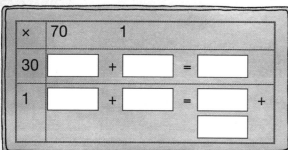

×	70	1	
30	___ + ___	= ___	
1	___ + ___	= ___	+
		___	

b 23 × 66

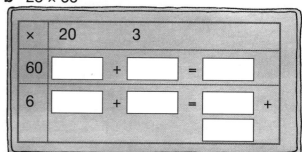

×	20	3	
60	___ + ___	= ___	
6	___ + ___	= ___	+
		___	

c 32 × 29

×	30	2	
20	___ + ___	= ___	
9	___ + ___	= ___	+
		___	

d 422 × 33

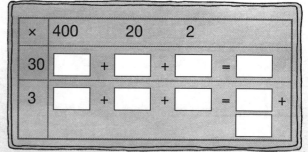

×	400	20	2	
30	___ + ___ + ___	= ___		
3	___ + ___ + ___	= ___	+	
			___	

Task 3

Hey presto! Starting completely from scratch, can you use the first method to solve these multiplication problems?

a 24 × 28

b 41 × 88

c 112 × 35

Task 4

Now for the second method! Work your magic on these!

a 77 × 17

b 145 × 15

Sorcerer's Skill Check

Well done! By now you probably have a favourite written method for multiplying large numbers. Practise it one last time with these problems!

a 26 × 41

b 105 × 29

That was tiring! Get yourself another silver shield
while we take a nap!

Word Problem Wizardry

Oh dear!
I find word problems so confusing! Pointy tells me they are just a way of putting maths problems into real life situations. He says I should take my time finding the numbers in the problem and deciding whether I need to add, subtract, divide or multiply to find the answer. Can you help me work these out?

Task 1 Rabracadada! Let's take Pointy's advice. Can you help me by deciding whether we need to add, subtract, multiply or divide to find the answer. When you've decided, write the symbol −, +, ×, ÷ in the jar.

a Pointy has a jar of 112 spiders. If 41 escape, how many will he have left?

b Mugly has £4 and Bugly has £2. How much do they have altogether?

c Wizard Whimstaff buys 6 boxes of Creepy Crabs' Claws. If each box contains 5 claws, how many claws will he have altogether?

d Mugly, Bugly and Pointy have 12 cakes to share. If they all eat the same number, how many cakes do each of them get?

Task 2 Wizard Whimstaff says it can be easier to rewrite problems with numbers instead of words. Pointy's done the first one to show you how.

a Miss Snufflebeam plays with 12 marbles and wins 4 more. How many does she have now? _____

b Wizard Whimstaff's cauldrons each hold 5 litres of potion. He has 6 cauldrons, so how much potion can he brew? _____

c Pointy has £25 and buys a new wand for £6. How much does he have left? _____

d Mugly and Bugly have baked 30 cakes. If they share them equally, how many will they each get? _____

Task 3

Help! If a word problem involves time, money or measures like weight or length, you need to take care to use the correct units. Can you pick the correct answers to these problems?

a Wizard Whimstaff has bought 6 metres of new rope for his rope trick. He cuts it in half. How long is each piece of rope?

3cm   4km   3m

2m   3km

b Pointy's watch stopped at 12.40. If it is 12.50 now, how long ago did the watch stop?

10 seconds   10 minutes   15 minutes

50 minutes   10 hours

Task 4

My head hurts! Some problems ask you more than one question and this can mean you have to solve extra maths problems. Can we try these together?

a Miss Snufflebeam has £50 to spend. If she buys a new hat for £12, how much will she have left? How many 50p toys will she be able to buy with the change?

_____

_____

b Pointy is painting the walls of the cave. He has worked out that he needs 12 litres of paint. If a tin of paint holds 5 litres, how many tins should he buy? How much paint will be left over?

_____

_____

Sorcerer's Skill Check

This is all so complicated! Can you help me practise with two more word problems?

a Pointy's collection of 100 bugs has escaped. He recaptures 60 straight away and another 32 later in a trap. How many are still on the loose?

b Wizard Whimstaff has given Mugly and Bugly £1 pocket money. They decide to save 40p and spend the rest on candied spiders. If the spiders cost 5p each, how many can they buy?

Hey Presto! Time for another silver shield!

Spellbinding Shapes

Maths Wizards know that once they can calculate the perimeter and area of simple rectangles, they can do the same for more complicated shapes.

 Perimeter
10 + 15 + 10 + 15 = 50cm
Area 10 × 15 = 150cm²

 Perimeter
6 + 12 + 6 + 12 = 36cm
Area 6 × 12 = 72cm²

This spell book has a perimeter of 50cm and an area of 150cm².

This one has a perimeter of 36cm and area of 72cm².

If you put them together it is called a compound shape. The new measurements look like this.

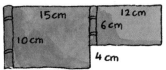

Perimeter
10 + 15 + 4 + 12 + 6 + 12 + 15
= 74cm

Area
15 × 10 = 150cm²
6 × 12 = 72cm²
222cm²

Task 1
Miss Snufflebeam has arranged her crystal collection into some compound shapes. Can you work out the perimeter and area of each one?

a
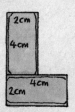

area:

perimeter:

b
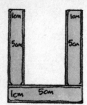

area:

perimeter:

c
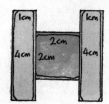

area:

perimeter:

Task 2
Super shape work so far, young apprentice! Can you split each shape up into rectangles, then calculate the area and perimeter? You'll need a ruler to find the measurements you need!

a area:

perimeter:

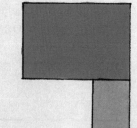

b area:

perimeter:

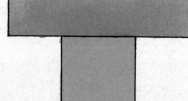

Task 3 Using a ruler, can you design your own compound shape, then calculate its perimeter and area?

area:

perimeter:

Task 4 Trace over these shapes, cut out the pieces and arrange them into four different compound shapes, without overlapping the pieces. Calculate the area and perimeter of each shape and put your answers in the table. What do you notice about the area of all your shapes? What things affect the perimeter?

Shape	Area	Perimeter
1	cm²	cm
2	cm²	cm
3	cm²	cm
4	cm²	cm

2 cm
8 cm

4 cm
4 cm

3 cm
2 cm

Sorcerer's Skill Check

Can you calculate the perimeter and area of this shape? Remember to work out the missing dimensions first on a separate sheet of paper!

area:

perimeter:

5 cm
2 cm
1 cm 1 cm 1 cm
2 cm 2 cm 2 cm

Burp! Your maths skills are in great shape, unlike us! Collect another silver shield!

Magical Measures

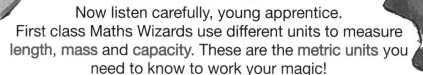

Now listen carefully, young apprentice. First class Maths Wizards use different units to measure length, mass and capacity. These are the metric units you need to know to work your magic!

Length: kilometres (km) metres (m) centimetres (cm) millimetres (mm)

Mass: kilograms (kg) grams (g)

Capacity: litres (l) millilitres (ml)

You may also come across old fashioned or imperial units like these in older spell books!

Length: yards (yd) feet (') inches (")

Mass: pounds (lb) ounces (oz)

Capacity: fluid ounces (fl oz) pints (pt)

Task 1 Metric measurements come in smaller and larger units to help you measure things of all sizes. Test your magic measurement powers by converting these smaller units into larger ones.

a 700cm = _____ m

b 20mm = _____ cm

c 2000m = _____ km

d 4000ml = _____ l

e 8000g = _____ kg

f 1200g = _____ kg

g 3000m = _____ km

h 200cm = _____ m

i 2000ml = _____ l

Task 2 Now let's go the other way. Wave your wand and convert these large units of measurement into smaller ones. Allakazan!

a 3cm = _____ mm

b 7l = _____ ml

c 4.5kg = _____ g

d 6.25km = _____ m

e 14.8m = _____ cm

f 3.89l = _____ ml

g 1.02kg = _____ g

h 1.4l = _____ ml

i 1m = _____ mm

Task 3
Well done! Now let's take a look at how imperial units compare with the metric units you've been working with. Use the table to help you work your magic and answer true or false to these questions.

Metric	Imperial
1cm	0.39 inches
1g	0.035 ounces
1kg	2.21 pounds
1l	1.76 pints

a 1lb of butter weighs more than 1kg of butter. _____

b A 6 inch ruler is roughly the same length as a 30cm ruler. _____

c In a recipe, 4oz of sugar would be roughly the same as 100g. _____

d 1 pint of milk is more than 1 litre of milk. _____

e If I bought a 1kg bag of flour, it would be enough for a recipe that needed 2lbs of flour. _____

Task 4
Now have a go at this exercise. Just pick the label you think fits best with each of the magical objects below. Hey presto!

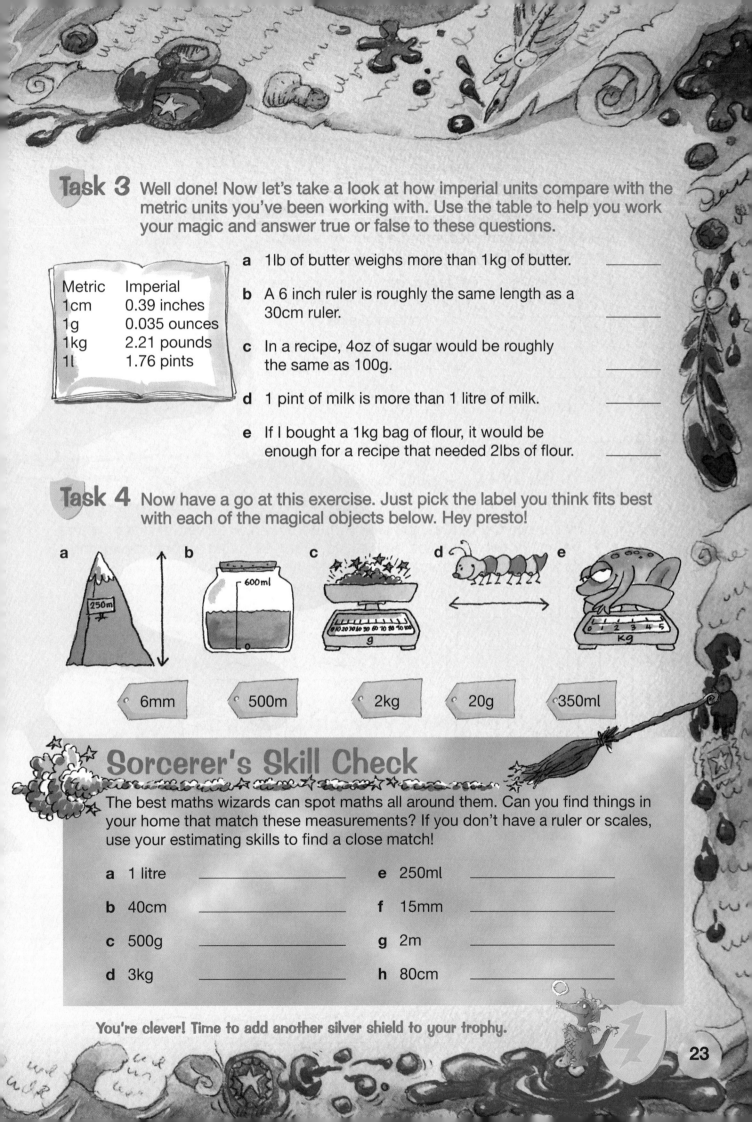

a   b   c   d   e

6mm   500m   2kg   20g   350ml

Sorcerer's Skill Check

The best maths wizards can spot maths all around them. Can you find things in your home that match these measurements? If you don't have a ruler or scales, use your estimating skills to find a close match!

a 1 litre _____   **e** 250ml _____

b 40cm _____   **f** 15mm _____

c 500g _____   **g** 2m _____

d 3kg _____   **h** 80cm _____

You're clever! Time to add another silver shield to your trophy.

Creepy Coordinates

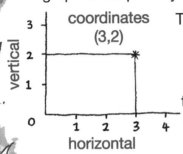

Slurp! **Coordinates** give you the information you need to find a point on a grid, graph or map. They come in two parts, like this:

coordinates (3,2)

The first number gives you the location of the point on the horizontal axis.

The second number locates the point on the vertical axis.

Burp!

Task 1 We're playing battleships with Pointy. To win, we need to guess where he has drawn the ships on his grid. Can you help us cheat by writing down the coordinates of his ships in the puddles?

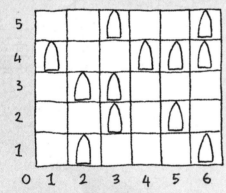

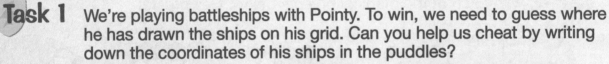

Task 2 Croak! Now we need to draw battleships on our own grid. Can you draw ships at these coordinates for us, while we tuck into our snack? Just make sure Pointy doesn't see!

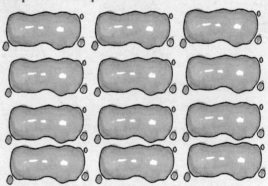

a	(4,2)	f	(1,5)
b	(1,3)	g	(4,3)
c	(6,2)	h	(5,3)
d	(6,5)	i	(4,4)
e	(2,5)	j	(1,2)

Task 3 Brain cell alert! Some grids have axes that represent negative numbers, too. Plot these coordinates, then join them up in alphabetical order to reveal the magic letter that starts the name of one of our friends.

a (–5, 5)

b (–3, –3)

c (0,5)

d (3, –3)

e (5,5)

Task 4 All this activity has made us sleepy! While we take a nap, can you choose a shape with straight sides, and plot it on this grid. Take care to match the corner points up with the grid. Then write down the coordinates of each point, for Pointy to check out later.

Sorcerer's Skill Check

Here's a plan of our lily pond. The lily pads in some squares aren't strong enough for us to sit on. Can you help us avoid a soaking by colouring the weak lily pads red? They are in squares (1,2), (3,2), (5,4), (4,2), (1,4).

Super plotting, young apprentice! Time to locate another silver shield.

Dazzling Data

Dabracababra! I hope I get this right! Line graphs are a good way of showing information, especially information about things that happen over a period of time. Apparently, because the points are joined up with a line, you can find information about what's going on between the points, too.

Plot the points first...   then join them up carefully.

Task 1 Wizard Whimstaff has left me to draw a line graph using the information in this chart. It shows how many buckets of rainwater have leaked through a crack in the cave roof. Can you do it for me?

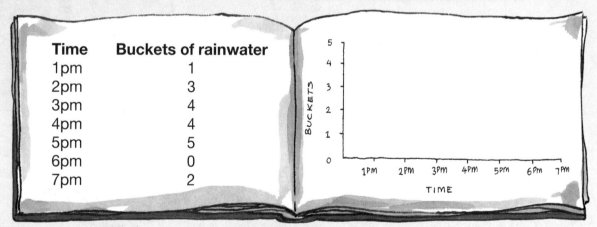

Time	Buckets of rainwater
1pm	1
2pm	3
3pm	4
4pm	4
5pm	5
6pm	0
7pm	2

Task 2 Help! Wizard Whimstaff loved your graph so much he wants us to answer these questions about the information it contains. Can you help me?

a   What time did the first bucket fill up?   _____

b   What time was it when 2 buckets were full?   _____

c   By 3pm, how many buckets of rainwater had been collected?   _____

d   What time do you think Pointy emptied all the buckets?   _____

e   How many buckets were full just before he emptied them?   _____

Task 3 These line graphs have been separated from the information below about what they represent. Draw a line to match them up again.

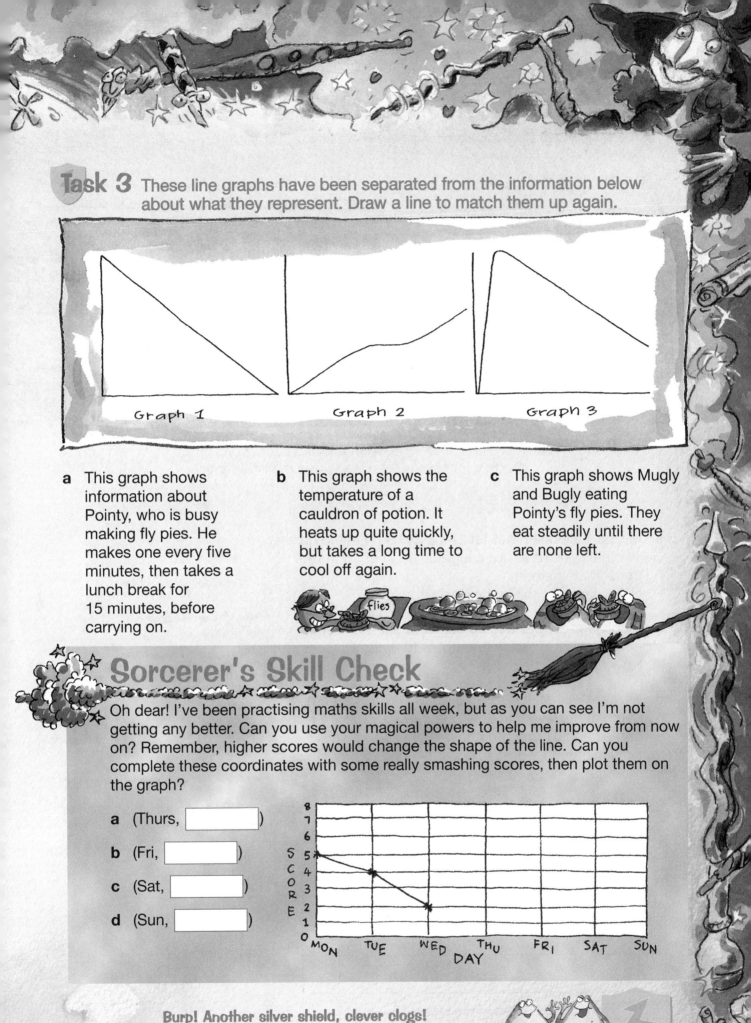

Graph 1   Graph 2   Graph 3

a This graph shows information about Pointy, who is busy making fly pies. He makes one every five minutes, then takes a lunch break for 15 minutes, before carrying on.

b This graph shows the temperature of a cauldron of potion. It heats up quite quickly, but takes a long time to cool off again.

c This graph shows Mugly and Bugly eating Pointy's fly pies. They eat steadily until there are none left.

Sorcerer's Skill Check

Oh dear! I've been practising maths skills all week, but as you can see I'm not getting any better. Can you use your magical powers to help me improve from now on? Remember, higher scores would change the shape of the line. Can you complete these coordinates with some really smashing scores, then plot them on the graph?

a (Thurs, ☐)

b (Fri, ☐)

c (Sat, ☐)

d (Sun, ☐)

Burp! Another silver shield, clever clogs!

27

Apprentice Wizard Challenge 2

Challenge 1 Use your favourite multiplication method to solve these problems.

a 42×56 **b** 21×78 **c** 23×85

Challenge 2 Pick the number problem that fits each word problem. When you've made your choice, can you solve the problems?

$$80 - (14 + 31) \qquad 24 - (2 \times 3) \qquad 28 - (6 + 6)$$

a Miss Snufflebeam has let 24 balloons off in the garden.
Two balloons have got caught in each of the three
trees in the garden.
How many are still in the sky?

=

b Mugly and Bugly have 28 cakes to eat. They each
eat six now, and save the others for later.
How many do they save?

=

c Wizard Whimstaff needs 80 potion bottles for a new
batch of his favourite spell. He currently has 14 red
bottles and 31 green bottles.
How many more bottles does he need to buy?

=

Challenge 3 Using a ruler, draw a compound shape in this space that is made up of three rectangles. Then calculate its area and perimeter.

area:

perimeter:

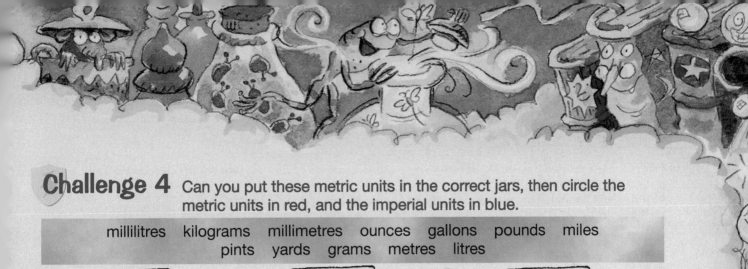

Challenge 4
Can you put these metric units in the correct jars, then circle the metric units in red, and the imperial units in blue.

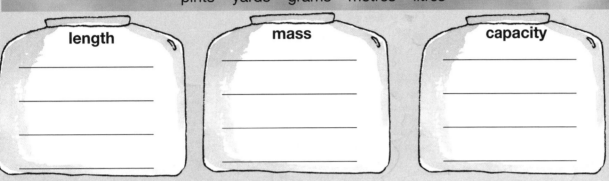

millilitres kilograms millimetres ounces gallons pounds miles
pints yards grams metres litres

length _____ _____ _____

mass _____ _____ _____

capacity _____ _____ _____

Challenge 5
Here are some ancient coordinates from an old spell book. Colour in the squares in each grid to reveal a magical number.

a (2,1), (2,5), (3,2), (3,5), (4,3), (4,5), (5,4), (5,5)

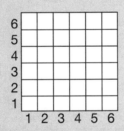

b (2,1), (2,4), (2,5, (2,6), (3,1), (3,4) (3,6), (4,1), (4,4) (4,6), (5,1), (5,2) (5,3), (5,4), (5,6)

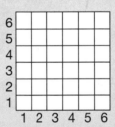

Challenge 6
This line graph shows the amount of money in Miss Snufflebeam's piggy bank over the course of several months. Use the data in the graph to answer these questions.

a Miss Snufflebeam starts saving in January with some money she was given for Christmas. How much was she given? _____

b How much had she saved in total by March? _____

c She stops saving for a couple of months. When is this? _____

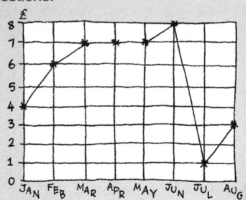

d In June she has more money in her piggy bank than at any other time. How much does she have? _____

Count how many challenges you got right and put stars on the test tube to show your score. Then take the last silver shield for your trophy!

6
5
4
3
2
1
Challenge Score

Answers

Pages 2–3

Task 1 a 1.13, 1.23, 1.32, 2.13, 2.23, 2.31
     b 14.14, 14.18, 14.81, 18.14,
        18.41, 18.84
     c 1.35, 1.55, 3.15, 3.51, 5.35, 5.53

Task 2 a 3.46   d 3.185
     b 12.22   e 5.246
     c 8.03   f 11.322

Task 3 a 2   g 3
     b 15   h 40
     c 1   i 13
     d 20   j 29
     e 3   k 13
     f 41   l 18

Task 4 a 1.26   f 26.304
     b 9.8   g 4.13
     c $18\frac{80}{100}$ h 12.13
     d $3\frac{1}{3}$ i $49\frac{3}{4}$
     e 6.7

Sorcerer's Skill Check

a 6.1, $6\frac{1}{3}$, $6\frac{3}{4}$, 6.8
b $4\frac{1}{4}$, 4.27, 4.62, $4\frac{3}{4}$
c 3.38, 3.4, $3\frac{2}{3}$, 3.7
d $1\frac{1}{8}$, 1.13, $1\frac{3}{8}$, 1.4

Pages 4–5

Task 1 a $4\frac{1}{4}$ e $4\frac{1}{8}$
     b $3\frac{1}{8}$ f $5\frac{2}{5}$
     c $1\frac{2}{7}$ g $2\frac{9}{12}$
     d $5\frac{1}{2}$ h $4\frac{1}{10}$

Task 2 a $\frac{1}{4}$ e $\frac{2}{3}$
     b $\frac{1}{3}$ f $\frac{2}{3}$
     c $\frac{1}{3}$ g $\frac{2}{3}$
     d $\frac{2}{3}$

Task 3 a $\frac{1}{5}, \frac{2}{5}, \frac{3}{5}, \frac{4}{5}$
     b $\frac{3}{10}, \frac{4}{10}, \frac{7}{10}, \frac{8}{10}$
     c $\frac{1}{6}, \frac{2}{6}, \frac{4}{6}, \frac{5}{6}$
     d $\frac{1}{5}, \frac{2}{5}, \frac{3}{5}, \frac{4}{5}$

Task 4 a 4   d 80
     b 9   e 12
     c 8

Sorcerer's Skill Check

a $\frac{13}{3} = 4\frac{1}{3}$ e $\frac{1}{3} = \frac{2}{6}$
b $\frac{9}{4} = 2\frac{1}{4}$ f $1\frac{1}{5} = \frac{6}{5}$
c $\frac{17}{5} = 3\frac{2}{5}$ g $\frac{30}{100} = \frac{3}{10}$
d $\frac{1}{10} = \frac{2}{20}$

Pages 6–7

Task 1 a 4:3   b 2:7
     c 1:4   d 2:4

Task 2 a 96:144   b 48:12
     c 18:24

Task 3 a 2 in 6   d 1 in 4
     b 4 in 9   e 3 in 10
     c 6 in 8   f 2 in 5

Task 4 a 3 slices shaded
     b 6 slices shaded
     c 4 slices shaded

Sorcerer's Skill Check

a 2:4 2 in 6   b 3:4 3 in 7
c 3:3 3 in 6   d 3:5 3 in 8

Pages 8–9

Task 1 a
     b
     c
     d
     e
     f

Task 2 a $\frac{1}{4}$ = 25%   e $\frac{20}{100}$ = 20%
     b $\frac{7}{10}$ = 70%   f $\frac{1}{2}$ = 50%
     c $\frac{4}{100}$ = 4%   g $\frac{30}{100}$ = 30%
     d $\frac{2}{3}$ = 66.6%

Task 3 a 50%   g 33.3%
     b 60%   h 30%
     c 20%   i 80%
     d 75%   j 90%
     e 40%   k 75%
     f 60%   l 25%

Task 4 a £5   f £72
     b £200   g £60
     c £180   h £450
     d £14   i £30
     e £400

Sorcerer's Skill Check

a $\frac{4}{10}$ e 10%
b 20%   f 50%
c 78%   g $\frac{9}{10}$
d 90%   h $\frac{2}{3}$

Pages 10–11

Task 1 a (3 + 4) = 7, 12 × 7 = 84
     b (4 − 2) = 2, 10 × 2 = 20
     c (6 − 4) = 2, 8 ÷ 2 = 4
     d (10 + 2) = 12, 36 ÷ 12 = 3
     e (4 × 2) = 8, 40 ÷ 8 = 5
     f (12 × 3) = 36, 12 + 36 = 48
     g (4 × 8) = 32, 64 − 32 = 32

Task 2 a 3 + (12 ÷ 2) = 9
     b 100 ÷ (12 − 2) = 10
     c 18 − (12 − 3) = 9
     d 21 ÷ (5 + 2) = 3
     e 3 × (2 + 2) = 12
     f 15 ÷ (10 ÷ 2) = 3
     g 12 − (4 + 1) = 7
     h 12 + (6 ÷ 2) = 15
     i 9 × (8 ÷ 2) = 36

Task 3 a 5 − 3 = 2   d 36 ÷ 4 = 9
     b 6 + 5 = 11   e 6 × 5 = 30
     c 6 ÷ 2 = 3   f 9 × 5 = 45

Task 4 Many answers are possible.

Sorcerer's Skill Check

a (2 × 2)   d (4 + 2)
b (5 + 2)   e (20 ÷ 2)
c (7 − 4)   f (16 ÷ 2)

Pages 12–13

Task 1 a 23.3   b 14.3
     c 44.3   d 71.9

Task 2 a 233   b 143
     c 443

Task 3 a 98.2   f 9112
     b 41.0   g 183.1
     c 1282   h 341
     d 120.4   i 1003
     e 1

Task 4 a, b, c, e, g and i are multiplied
     by 10
     d, f and h are multiplied by 100

Sorcerer's Skill Check

a 1.01   f 0.1234
b 7.341   g 0.9431
c 1.894   h 1.212
d 0.13   i 3.144
e 4.174   j 7.12

Pages 14–15

Challenge 1

a 63.84, 64.38, 64.83, 68.34, (68.43)
b 71.19, 71.49, 71.91, 71.94, (71.98)
c 67.381, 67.814, 68.183, 68.813,
  (68.816)
d 70.143, 70.413, 71.314, 71.911,
  (71.918)
e 70.013, 70.908, 71.103, 71.919,
  (71.991)

Challenge 2

a $\frac{7}{2}, 3\frac{1}{2}$ f $\frac{44}{5}, 8\frac{4}{5}$
b $\frac{25}{4}, 6\frac{1}{4}$ g $\frac{19}{8}, 2\frac{3}{8}$
c $\frac{5}{3}, 1\frac{2}{3}$ h $\frac{14}{3}, 4\frac{2}{3}$
d $\frac{49}{4}, 12\frac{1}{4}$ i $\frac{36}{5}, 7\frac{1}{5}$
e $\frac{15}{7}, 2\frac{1}{7}$ j $\frac{103}{8}, 12\frac{7}{8}$

Challenge 3

a 3   b 4
c 8   d 12

Challenge 4
a	£24	**f**	£84
b	£16	**g**	£90
c	£90	**h**	£162
d	£12	**i**	£110
e	£32		

Challenge 5
- **a** $3 \times (4 + 2) = 3 \times 6 = 18$
- **b** $27 - (21 \div 3) = 27 - 7 = 20$
- **c** $10 \times (12 - 8) = 10 \times 4 = 40$
- **d** $24 - (9 - 4) = 24 - 5 = 19$
- **e** $12 \times (2 \times 4) = 12 \times 8 = 96$
- **f** $8 \div (6 - 4) = 8 \div 2 = 4$
- **g** $2 + (18 \div 2) = 2 + 9 = 11$
- **h** $36 \div (3 + 3) = 36 \div 6 = 6$
- **i** $49 \div (21 \div 3) = 49 \div 7 = 7$
- **j** $7 \times (3 \times 3) = 7 \times 9 = 63$

Challenge 6
- **a** $1.4 \times 10 = 14$; $1.4 \times 100 = 140$
- **b** $0.41 \times 10 = 4.1$; $0.41 \times 100 = 41$
- **c** $3.031 \times 10 = 30.31$; $3.031 \times 100 = 303.1$
- **d** $0.048 \times 10 = 0.48$; $0.048 \times 100 = 4.8$

Pages 16–17
Task 1	**a**	2145	**b**	1007
	c	2340		
Task 2	**a**	2201	**b**	1518
	c	928	**d**	13926
Task 3	**a**	672	**b**	3608
	c	3920		
Task 4	**a**	1309	**b**	2175

Sorcerer's Skill Check
a	1066	**b**	3045

Pages 18–19
Task 1	**a**	–	**b**	+
	c	×	**d**	÷

Task 2
- **a** $12 + 4 = 16$
- **b** 5 litres × 6 = 30 litres
- **c** £25 – £6 = £19
- **d** $30 \div 2 = 15$

Task 3
a	3m	**b**	10 minutes

Task 4
- **a** £50 – £12 = £38 left
  £38 ÷ 50p = 76 toys
- **b** $12 \div 5 = 2\frac{2}{5}$, so he should buy
  3 cans of paint.
  3 × 5 = 15 litres of paint.
  15 – 12 = 3 litres left over.

Sorcerer's Skill Check
a	8	**b**	12

Pages 20–21
Task 1
- **a** Area = 16cm²
  Perimeter = 20cm
- **b** Area = 15cm²
  Perimeter = 32cm
- **c** Area = 12cm²
  Perimeter = 20cm

Task 2
- **a** Area = 8cm²
  Perimeter = 14cm
- **b** Area = 11cm²
  Perimeter = 18cm

Task 3 Many answers are possible.

Task 4 Many answers are possible. The area of all compound shapes will be 38cm². The perimeter will vary according to how the shapes are joined.

Sorcerer's Skill Check
Area = 16cm²
Perimeter = 26cm

Pages 22–23
Task 1
	a	7m	**f**	1.2kg
	b	2cm	**g**	3km
	c	2km	**h**	2m
	d	4l	**i**	2l
	e	8kg		

Task 2
	a	30mm	**f**	3890ml
	b	7000ml	**g**	1020g
	c	4500g	**h**	1400ml
	d	6250m	**i**	1000mm
	e	1480cm		

Task 3 **a**, **b** and **d** are false
c and **e** are true

Task 4
	a	500m	**b**	350ml
	c	20g	**d**	6mm
	e	2kg		

Sorcerer's Skill Check
Many answers are possible.

Pages 24–25
Task 1 Pointy's battleships can be found in these squares: (1,4) (2,1) (2,3) (3,2) (3,3) (3,5) (4,4) (5,2) (5,4) (6,1) (6,4) (6,5)

Task 2
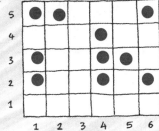

Task 3 The magic letter is W.

Task 4 Many answers are possible.

Sorcerer's Skill Check
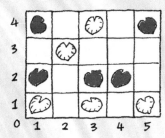

Pages 26–27
Task 1
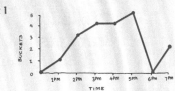

Task 2
- **a** 1pm
- **b** 1.30pm or 7pm
- **c** 4
- **d** 6pm
- **e** 5

Task 3
a	Graph 2	**b**	Graph 3
c	Graph 1		

Sorcerer's Skill Check
Many answers are possible.

Pages 28–29
Challenge 1
a	2352	**b**	1638
c	1955		

Challenge 2
- **a** $24 - (2 \times 3) = 18$
- **b** $28 - (6 + 6) = 16$
- **c** $80 - (14 + 31) = 35$

Challenge 3
Many answers are possible.

Challenge 4
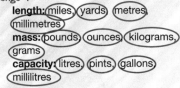

Challenge 5
- **a** The magical number is 7.
- **b** The magical number is 5.

Challenge 6
- **a** £4
- **b** £7
- **c** March and April
- **d** £8

The end

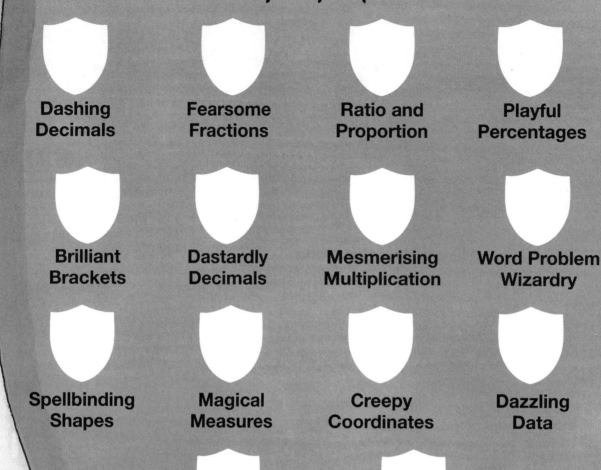

Wizard's Trophy of Excellence

Dashing Decimals

Fearsome Fractions

Ratio and Proportion

Playful Percentages

Brilliant Brackets

Dastardly Decimals

Mesmerising Multiplication

Word Problem Wizardry

Spellbinding Shapes

Magical Measures

Creepy Coordinates

Dazzling Data

Apprentice Wizard Challenge 1

Apprentice Wizard Challenge 2

This is to state that Wizard Whimstaff awards

Apprentice _____

the Trophy of Maths Wizardry. Congratulations!

Published 2002

10 9 8 7 6 5

Letts Educational
4 Grosvenor Place, London SW1X 7DL
School enquiries: 01539 564910
Parent & student enquiries: 01539 564913
E-mail: mail@lettsed.co.uk Website: www.letts-educational.com

Text, design and illustrations © Letts Educational Ltd 2002

Author: Alison Head
Book Concept and Development:
Helen Jacobs, Publishing Director; Sophie London, Project Editor
Series Editor: Lynn Huggins-Cooper
Design and Editorial: 2idesign ltd, Cambridge
Cover Design: Linda Males
Illustrations: Mike Phillips and Neil Chapman (Beehive Illustration)
Cover Illustration: Neil Chapman

British Library Cataloguing in Publication Data

A CIP record for this book is available from the British Library.

ISBN 978-1-84315-128-9

Printed and bound in Italy

Colour reproduction by PDQ Digital Media Solutions Limited,
Bungay, Suffolk.